This Book Belongs To...

....

....

....

Cutting a lonely figure on a country lane is the winter postie. His hat could be a target for a snowball but not if he was delivering your Beano.

This book tries to capture the fabulous excitement that ran through every child when the curtains were flung open to reveal that a fresh blanket of snow had fallen in the night.

The shout of "It's been snowing!" started a mass exodus outside to build snowmen and throw snowballs at everything and anyone.

With this in mind the Beano and Dandy golden age archive present their own brand of Winter Games. No, this is not the Winter Olympics, this is snowballing, sledging, sliding, skating and skiing where the big prize is having fun.

The Editor

IN THIS WINTER WONDERLAND ARE:

Dennis the Menace
The Banana Bunch
Minnie the Minx
Corporal Clott
Biffo the Bear
Korky the Cat
Big Head and Thick Head
Bully Beef and Chips
Desperate Dan
Little Plum
Bash Street Kids
Roger the Dodger
Lord Snooty
Billy Whizz
Ginger
Pop, Dick and Harry
The Three Bears
Tin Lizzie
The Crackaway Twins
Willie Fixit
Smasher
Winker Watson
Billy the Cat.

I hope that's not your Dad's best hat and your Grandma's pipe you're using?

THE
WINTER GAMES
PHOTO
ALBUM

MINNIE the MINX

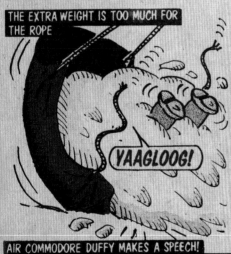

THIS OLD AERO-ENGINE WILL MAKE A QUICK JOB OF CLEARING AWAY THE SNOW!

YIPPEE! IT'S WORKING A TREAT!

WHIRR!

WHAT ON EARTH'S GOING ON OUT THERE?

NOW TO SWING THE TARPAULIN ROUND THE CORNER AND DUMP THE SNOW.

YAHOO!

SCOOP!

AIR COMMODORE DUFFY ARRIVES

FIRST, WE'LL GO TO THE MESS FOR A MEAL, COMMODORE!

GOOD IDEA, GRUMBLY!

I'D BETTER SHOVEL AWAY THE SNOW THAT'S DRIFTING UNDER THE CANOPY.

GOODNESS! IT'S BLOWING A BLIZZARD NOW!

A LITTLE LATER

AH! CLOTT HAS MADE A GOOD JOB OF KEEPING THE PATH CLEAR!

ME, GROAN!

MOAN!

CRUMBS! TIME I WASN'T HERE!

GURR! WE'LL SOON SPOT CLOTT FROM THE AIR, COMMODORE!

DAN 16.2.74

THE SNOW'S ALL GONE, BUT THERE'S A FUNNY LOOKING SNOWMAN DOWN BELOW—AND I THINK I RECOGNISE IT.

HO-HO! THEY'VE PASSED OVERHEAD AND I DON'T THINK THEY NOTICED ME!

Spend a **LAUGH-HOUR** with "The BEANO" funsters

THE BEANO

No. 861. Jan. 17th, 1959. 2ᴰ

EVERY THURSDAY

Ah, remember good old glass milk bottles delivered to your doorstep on a winter's morn. You couldn't get the milk out of the bottle it was frozen solid. Bet the milkboy's fingers weren't much better.

A LAUGH OR A THRILL IN EVERY INCH

THE DANDY

2ᴰ

EVERY TUESDAY

No. 891—DEC. 20th, 1958.

KORKY THE CAT

Come and have a joyride, boys,
On Korky's sledging run!
Join with him and all his pals
In a basinful of fun!

WOW!

OOPS!

The first scene from this Dennis, sums up the feeling this cartoon collection is celebrating.

Printed and Published in Great Britain by D. C. THOMSON & CO., Ltd., and JOHN LENG & Co., Ltd., 12 Fetter Lane, Fleet Street, London, E.C.4. © D. C. THOMSON & CO., LTD., 1965

BIG HEAD AND THICK HEAD

A Bully Beef set by J C (Jimmy) Hughes. Bully Beef and Chips was Jimmy's favourite out of the many characters he drew. He got fun developing imaginative ways to beat the Bully.

Bah! The teacher's watching so you can't throw a snowball at the stupid photographer.

This page is a scan of an etcher's proof, the last chance the Editor had of seeing the strip before it went to the Printers. Each proof was signed and dated by the Editor — in this case Harold Cramond, Beano Editor 1959 — 84.

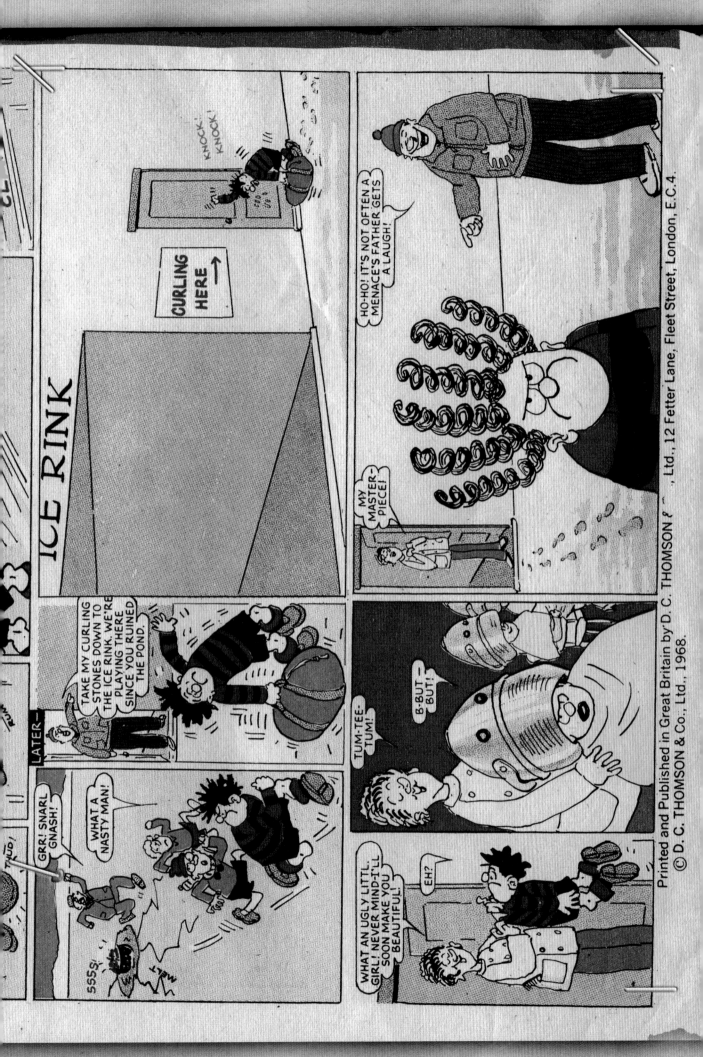

Printed and Published in Great Britain by D. C. THOMSON & ...., Ltd., 12 Fetter Lane, Fleet Street, London, E.C.4.
© D. C. THOMSON & Co., Ltd., 1968.

From The McTickles, 1975 Beano Book.

We live in the Highlands and we've never seen a haggis yet. Then again, we can't see anything.

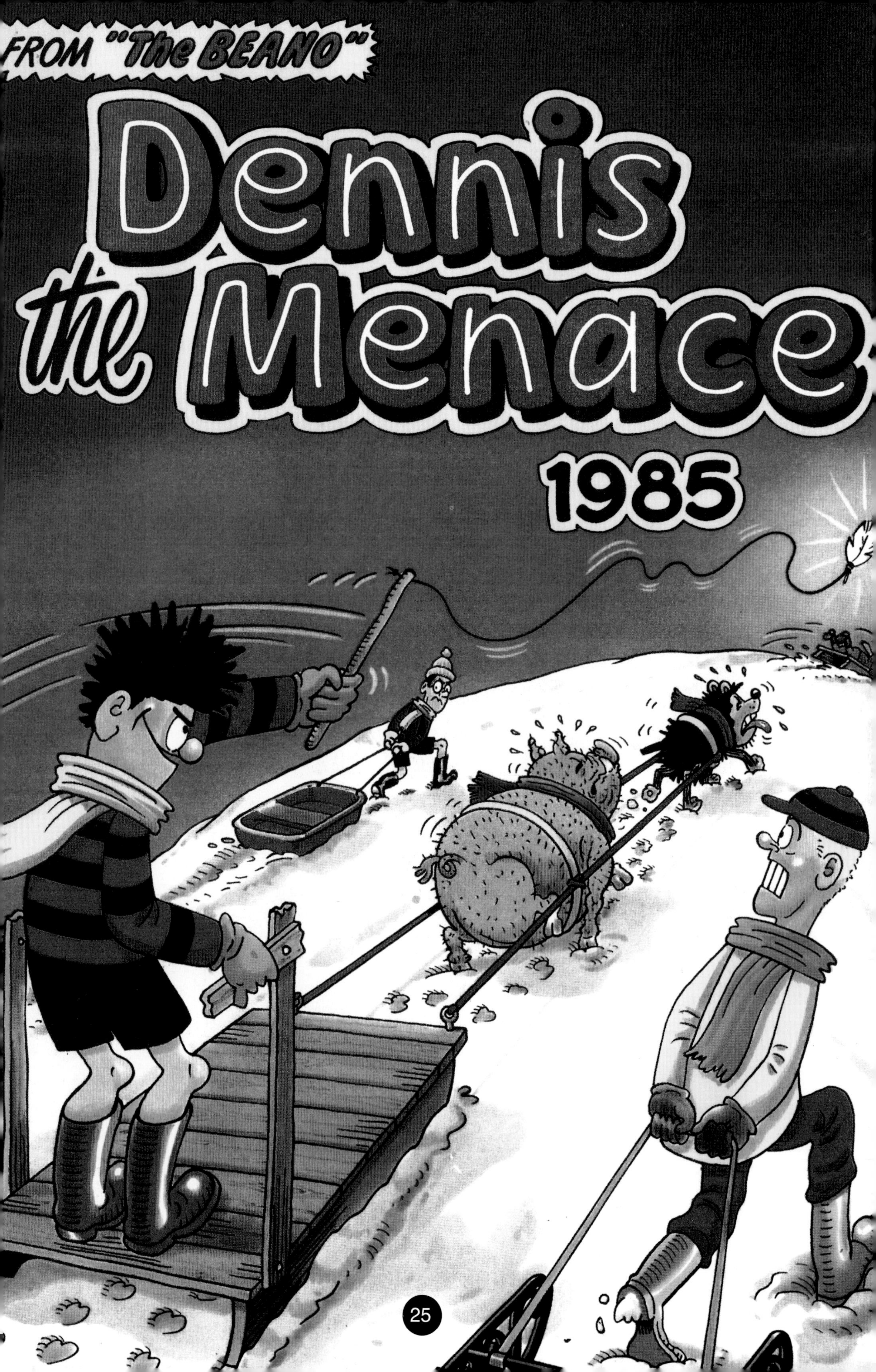
FROM "The BEANO"
Dennis the Menace
1985

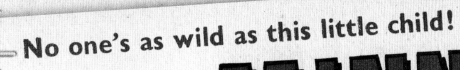

MINNIE the MINX

Artist Jim Petrie drew this 'Minnie on ice' Beano Book set. Jim was a master of action cartoon work, many of the poses coming from observing his own kids at play.

Ice-hockey's tough when Minnie plays rough!

Desperate Dan's snowball fight is one of the funniest stories to appear in The Dandy during 1961. The action takes place in Dan's unusual wild west home town of Cactusville with its British postboxes, Mayor and milestones.

I've thrown a
snowball into the air,
where it lands I do
not care.
(On your head most
likely, you little
twit!)

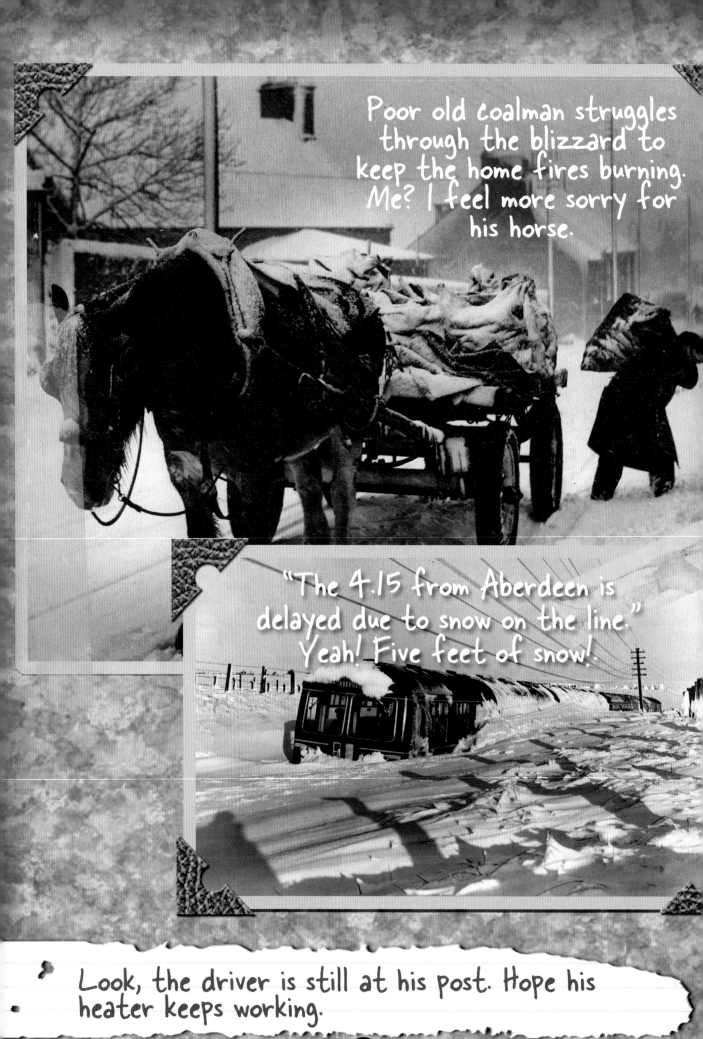

Poor old coalman struggles through the blizzard to keep the home fires burning. Me? I feel more sorry for his horse.

"The 4.15 from Aberdeen is delayed due to snow on the line." Yeah! Five feet of snow!

Look, the driver is still at his post. Hope his heater keeps working.

THE BASH STREET KIDS

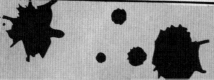

Present ☑

WILFRID

Present ☑

SIDNEY

Present ☑

HERBERT

Present ☑

SMIFFY

Present ☑

TOOTS

Present ☑

DANNY

Present ☑

PLUG

Present ☑

☑

FATTY

✗ Last seen 1959

JIMMY

✗ Last seen 1959

ELLA

✗ Last seen 1960

TEDDY

Just how bad were Jimmy, Ella and Teddy to get excluded from Bash Street School?

SCHOOL BELL

Almost every inch of white drawing board was inked to produce this hilariously packed Bash Street strip. Wonderful work by artist Leo Baxendale.

One of my favourite Bash Street classroom scenes ever is the second frame in this story where the snowman teacher is sitting almost unnoticed amongst the pupils. Another marvellous page drawn by Leo Baxendale.

Not really winter but the kids are well frozen!

A great Bash Street expedition. Drawn by Dave Sutherland.
Sir Edward Pillory looks like a ginger-haired Teacher.

PUPILS, THIS IS SIR EDWARD PILLORY, WHO WILL GIVE YOU A LECTURE ON CLIMBING IN THE HIM-AHUM!-HIMIL-HUMPH!-ER-MOUNTAINS IN INDIA.

HERO WORSHIP

ON WITH THE LECTURE—

—AND THERE IN THE SNOW WE SAW THESE GIGANTIC FOOTPRINTS!

GASP!

—AND THROUGH THE SNOW-STORM LOOMED THIS HUGE FIGURE!

ERK! WHAT WAS IT, SIR EDWARD?

DANNY'S DADS BOOTS

TOOTH PICK

SUDDENLY—

AGH! GIGANTIC FOOTPRINTS!

THEN—

G-GASP! IT'S THE ABOMINABLE SNOWMAN!

BUT— AW, NO! IT'S JUST THE ABOMINABLE DUSTMAN!

GRR! WHO ARE YOU CALLING "ABOMINABLE"? SCAT BEFORE I REPORT YOU TO YOUR TEACHER!

PHEW!

SO—

ER—I'M NOT SURE IF THIS IS A "GRANNY" KNOT OR A "GRANDAD" KNOT!

BUT SMIFFY'S KNOT IS NOT A KNOT—

BUNNY IGLOO

GASP! IT WAS EVEN MORE ABOMINABLE THAN I THOUGHT IT WOULD BE!

LATER—

EXTRA! EXTRA! EVEREST EXPEDITION FINDS ABOMINABLE SNOWMAN ON BASH STREET HILL!

ABOMINABLE SNOWMAN SEEN ON BASH ST. HILL

HUH! WHAT ROTTEN LUCK! WE WERE UP THERE, TOO, AND WE NEVER SAW A THING!

Minnie the Minx

Tee-hee! Tee-hee! The pals try to ski!

LORD SNOOTY AND HIS PALS

Although not signed, this Lord Snooty set was drawn by legendary artist Dudley D Watkins for Beano Book 1967. It has all of the old world charm he gave to the original Snooty in 1938.

Snow at last, thick and fast!

Lots of gags in this Billy Whizz winter spread. Drawn by Mal Judge who was famous for his newspaper cartoons.

Biffo loved skiing and lots of his covers were set on the slopes.

"LAUGH"-TIME

THE BEANO

No. 752. DEC. 15th, 1956. 2ᴰ

EVERY THURSDAY

BIFFO *the* **BEAR**

WATCH THAT TREE, BUSTER!

CRASH!

WATCH THAT BOULDER BIFFO!

CRUNCH

WELL, WE GOT TO THE BOTTOM OF THE SLOPE— —SOMEHOW!

LET'S CLIMB UP TO THE TOP AND TRY AGAIN!

WE KNOW WHAT TO LOOK OUT FOR THIS TIME, FOLKS!

LET'S GO!

WHIZZ! WHIZZ!

HO! HO!

HO! HO!

WHAT'S GOING ON?

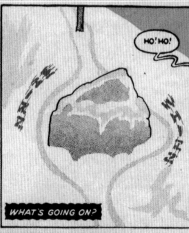

HO! HO! FOOLED YOU, READERS!

By 1967 Biffo is setting ski records!

Billy so loved speed that skiing was a perfect winter spow
for him. This set from the Beano Book of 1971.

I take my thermal hat off to this early postlady. No heated 4x4 delivery van for her — just a bike and wellies and a grim hatred for the weather.

Billy goes like the breeze on his runaway skis!

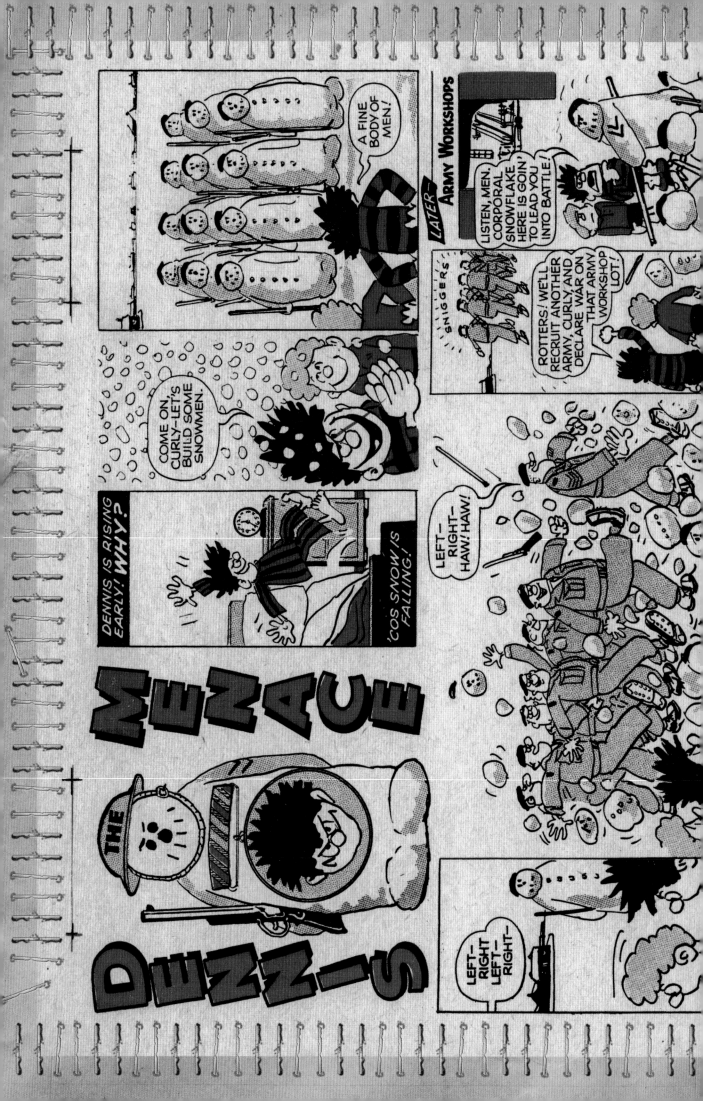

The Beezer BOOK 1969

The Beezer and Topper comics come from the same department as Beano and Dandy. This snowy cover featuring Ginger was drawn by Dudley D Watkins.

Robert Nixon
[dr]ew this charming
[c]over of Beezer
[star]s at play.

A mischievous Ginger this time drawn by Bob McGrath.

THE Beezer BOOK 1970

Into the teeth of the storm struggles the butcher's delivery boy. Never mind the raging blizzard – Mrs Simmonds needs her pork sausages by 4pm prompt!

POP DICK and HARRY

HELLO, BOYS!

P-POP!

POP PULLS OUT THE WEDGE—

ANY MINUTE NOW! HEH-HEH!

JUST THEN—

WHAT'S POP DOING UP HERE, ANY-WAY?

SMACK!

EH?

HO-HO-HO!

WH-WH-WHAT? OH, NO! HELP! H---

AARGH!

WHUMP!

THAT WAS A SUPER SNOWBALL TRAP, POP! HAVE ANOTHER ONE JUST FOR LUCK! HO-HO!

THE THREE BEARS

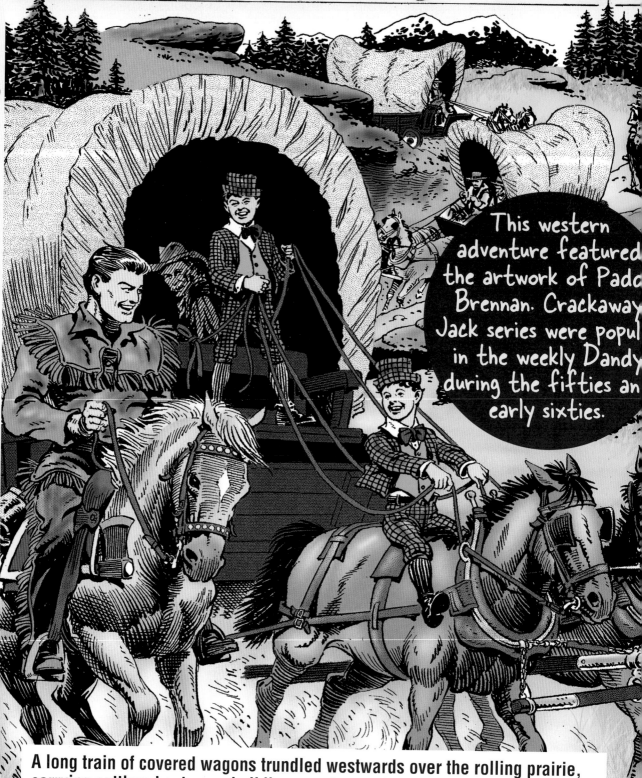

The CRACKAWAY TWIN'

This western adventure featured the artwork of Pado Brennan. Crackaway Jack series were popul in the weekly Dandy during the fifties an early sixties.

A long train of covered wagons trundled westwards over the rolling prairie, carrying settlers bent upon building new homes in a new land. At the head of the train rode Crackaway Jack, the fearless frontier scout. And in his special care were two of the most reckless, mischievous lads he had ever met in all his wanderings. They were the Turpin Twins, Rocky and Roly Turpin. Jack was keeping a watchful eye on them as they drove the leading wagon.

But it was too cold today for mischief. A blizzard blew up. Muffled against the driving snow. Crackaway Jack led the wagon train on into the teeth of it.

The snow deepened. The horses were struggling. Crackaway Jack was thinking of halting for the day when the leading wagon stopped. The horses had sunk in a drift.

It was a big job freeing them, but Jack had many helpers. Rocky stood shivering in the cold. But Roly found something to do. He made snowballs!

SMACK! His first throw scored a bull's-eye – on Rocky's neck!

"Ha-ha!" Brilliant good fun! But Rocky took it badly. He whirled round in a fury and scraped up some snow.

Hastily, Roly slung another snowball to stop Rocky's attack. His aim was no good with his left hand. He missed.

But Rocky didn't! At close range he scored a direct hit on Roly's face!

The brothers flew at each other. Fists flailing, they tumbled over and over in the soft snow, punching so furiously that Crackaway Jack came running.

The scout tore the battlers apart. "He started it!" shouted Rocky. "Tell-tale!" jeered Roly. "Cut it out, both of you!" rapped Crackaway Jack. "I want no more trouble from you two."

The scout went back to the wagon. But the Turpin twins stayed put – on separate rocks. They weren't speaking to each other now.

But when Roly started scraping snow together at the top of a ridge, Rocky sneaked a look.

Oh, so Roly was making a snowman! Huh! But not a bad idea. Rocky climbed down from his perch and started rolling a big snowball to make a head.

Their feud forgotten, the twins fitted the head on to the body. That was one snowman completed. Working together the twins made several more.

Rocky was sticking on stone buttons when he got the fright of his life. An arrow suddenly shot past his ear.

"Sioux!" shouted the Turpins, and they rushed for the wagons as hard as they could go. The settlers came at the double.

Crackaway Jack and his men flung themselves down behind the line of snowmen, using them as a rampart from which to fire down at the warriors.

The situation for the settlers was serious. They were short of ammunition! What could they do? In desperation Roly snatched the head off a snowman and heaved it at the enemy

Crackaway Jack's eyes lit up. This was the answer! "Heave over the snowmen," shouted the scout. Down the hill rolled the snowman "army"!

But when Roly pushed over his snowman, his feet slipped – and he went with it!

As the snowman rolled over, Roly became embedded in it and unable to move. The snowman gathered more snow with every yard until it turned into a monster snowball with Roly stuck in it. CRACK! His flying foot flattened the advancing warriors. The same thing was happening all along the line. The warriors were bowled over, left, right and centre by the lumbering masses of snow. And behind the snowmen charged Crackaway Jack and the settlers.

Roly Turpin's downhill tumble came to an end when the giant snowball broke up. Bruised and breathless, Roly found himself in deadly danger. Crackaway Jack could do no more than scoop up some snow.

WHAM! He heaved the handful of snow at the warrior, blinding him.

Crackaway Jack leapt into action while he was still clawing the snow from his face.

Meanwhile, the warriors who had survived the charge of the snowmen were put to flight.

That night there was laughter round the camp fire. And the settlers drank a toast in steaming coffee to the Turpin twins, and especially to Roly Turpin, the plucky lad whose accidental charge had helped to save the whole wagon train!

DESPERATE DAN

SOLID RED GROUND — BLUE LET[T]

SNORE~GRUNT~THERE'S SOMETHING TICKLING MY NOSE~ A-A-AH~

TICKLE

A-A-AH

TISHOO

GOSH! WHERE AM I? I SEEM TO BE SLEEPING OUT IN THE OPEN!~ NO, I'M IN MY BEDROOM, BUT THE ROOF HAS DISAPPEARED, AND EVERYTHING'S COVERED WITH SNOW!

A-A-AH-TISHOO

DRAT IT! I'VE GOT A PESKY COLD. I'LL STAND ON THE BED AND GET DRESSED.

WHERE ARE MY TROUSERS AND BOOTS? HOW CAN I FIND THEM UNDER SIX FEET OF SNOW?

I GIVE UP. I'LL GO TO THE DOCTOR, GET HIM TO FIX MY COLD AND BUY A PAIR OF TROUSERS ON THE WAY.

I'VE GOT MYSELF WRAPPED UP IN A BLANKET BECAUSE OF MY COLD~AW GEE! ALL THE SHOPS ARE UNDER THE SNOW, AND I CAN'T TELL WHICH IS THE TAILOR'S.

SURGERY

AH! THERE'S THE DOCTOR'S HOUSE. I'LL CALL THERE FIRST.

IN THE DOCTOR'S GOT A COLD, DAN? YOU MUST BE CODDLING YOURSELF. TUT-TUT! FANCY WEARING A BLANKET ON TOP OF ALL YOUR CLOTHES!

W-W-WELL, NOT EXACTLY ALL MY CLOTHES, DOC.

The original boards of a classic Desperate Dan.
I love the sneeze making the bear jump out of his skin.

SOLID RED X   Take out Keyline   BLUE LETTERING

Poor old Dan lost his pants, size ninety-nine;
But he soon gets some more — mighty fine!
When he sneezes in the night
Grizzly bear leaps up in fright,
Saying, "Please, sir! Furry pants, sir! Lend you mine!"

SHUCKS, IF I'M CODDLING MYSELF I'D BETTER THROW AWAY MY BLANKET. BUT I'LL HAVE TO FIND ME A PAIR OF PANTS AND SOME BOOTS.

I'VE PULLED MY HAT OVER MY EYES TO KEEP THE WIND FROM BLOWING IT OFF, AND NOW I CAN HARDLY SEE.

SNAP

IT'S A PESKY COLD NIGHT ~ AND WHAT A BITING WIND! I FEEL IT BITING MY FINGERS! DRAT IT, I'M GOING TO SNEEZE AGAIN ~ A-A-AH ~

BITE

-TISHOO

THERE I GO AGAIN!

LIGHT

SCARED

I CAN'T STOP SNEEZING A-A-AH ~

-TISHOO

I SCARED THAT BEAR SO MUCH THAT HE JUMPED OUT OF HIS SKIN, HO! COME BACK! YOU'VE LEFT YOUR FURRY TROUSERS!

WELL, IF HE DOESN'T WANT THEM THEY'LL DO VERY WELL FOR ME!

OH ~ MY COLD ~ A-A-AH ~ TISHOO.

I'M SNEEZING ALL THE SNOW AWAY ~ HULLO! THERE'S A HOUSE WITH NO ROOF!

AH! HERE'S A GUN-HOLSTER ~ AND A NATTY PAIR OF TROUSERS AND BOOTS AS WELL. I GUESS I'LL WEAR THESE AND KEEP THE FURRY ONES FOR SUNDAY.

SAY, WAIT A MINUTE! THESE ARE MY TROUSERS. HERE'S MY PENKNIFE, THE BUTTON AND THE FOREIGN COIN I HAD IN MY POCKET.

A-A-AH ~ TISHOO

SHUCKS! AND I HAVEN'T GOT A COLD EITHER ~ THAT'S A FEATHER I'VE SNEEZED OUT. IT'S BEEN TICKLING MY NOSE ALL THE TIME!

D. WATKINS

Four weekly Desperate Dans from the sixties. The stories were all written by Albert Barnes, the Dandy Editor.

Dan loves his horse, it must be said — Except when it occupies his bed!

Desperate DAN

IT'S BEEN SNOWING AGAIN. I SAY, WHAT ARE THOSE FUNNY LOOKING HUMPS BESIDE THE LAMP-POST?

OH! I FORGOT! THAT'S MY HORSE. I TIED IT TO THE LAMP-POST.

IT'LL BE FROZEN STIFF!

YOU'D BETTER BRING IT IN AND THAW IT OUT IN FRONT OF THE FIRE, DAN!

I'LL HAVE TO GET MY HANDS UNDERNEATH ITS TUMMY AND LIFT IT!

OOPS! WHY, IT'S BROUGHT BITS OF THE PAVEMENT UP WITH IT!

I'LL HOLD THE POOR BRUTE IN FRONT OF THE FIRE TO MELT THE ICE!

WE NEED SOMETHING BIGGER TO CATCH THE DRIPS THOUGH, DAN.

JUST A MINUTE, AUNT AGGIE, I'LL GET THE BATH!

WE'LL BE ALL RIGHT NOW.

THAT'S BETTER, DAN.

WE MIGHT AS WELL SIT AND READ WHILE THE HORSE THAWS OUT.

YES, IT'S NICE TO SIT BACK WITH A BOOK AND GET MY FEET UP!

PRESENTLY THE HORSE STIRS. A HOOF HAS BEEN BLOCKING UP THE PLUG.

THE HOUSE BEGINS TO BE FLOODED AND IN FLOATS A WOODEN TRAY FULL OF CAKES.

WHAT'S THIS? THE ROOM FULL OF WATER AND THE HORSE JUST EATING THE LAST OF OUR TEA CAKES!

HOW DID THAT HAPPEN? THE HORSE MUST HAVE HAD ITS FOOT OVER THE PLUG-HOLE, THEN MOVED IT! I'LL BAIL OUT THROUGH THE WINDOW.

GET INTO THE LOBBY WHILE WE GET RID OF THE WATER.

OPEN THE FRONT DOOR AND LET THE WATER OUT.

BETTER HOLD THE CARPET UP IN FRONT OF THE FIRE TO DRY IT.

WRING OUT THE FLOOR CLOTH IN THE BATH!

AT LAST—WE CAN GET ON WITH OUR READING.

I'VE JUST REMEMBERED—WHERE'S THE HORSE?

YES! WHERE IS IT?

IT'S NOT HERE—SURELY IT MUST'VE GONE UPSTAIRS!

WE PUT IT IN THE LOBBY.

HO-HO-HO! LOOK! IT'S ASLEEP IN UNCLE DAN'S BED!

HUH! IT'S NOT STAYING THERE A MINUTE LONGER!

YOU LEAVE THAT POOR HORSE ALONE! AFTER ALL IT'S BEEN THROUGH, SURELY YOU CAN SLEEP IN THE HORSE'S STABLE!

A COW PIE A DAY KEEPS HUNGER AWAY

SO—IN THE STABLE

IT GETS TO SLEEP IN MY BED AND EAT MY CAKES! WHAT A CHEEK! I'LL EAT ITS HAY FOR THAT!

HORSE BLANKET

MUNCH

Next week — The Sheriff's horse is ill but Dan is not idle — The desperate man wears a bit and a bridle!

Next week — You know Dan's tough, so you needn't have fears — When you see flames coming out of his ears!

94

One of the many stories that artist Bill Holroyd produced for The Dandy. His busy multi-character style of drawing helped give the Dandy its distinctive style.

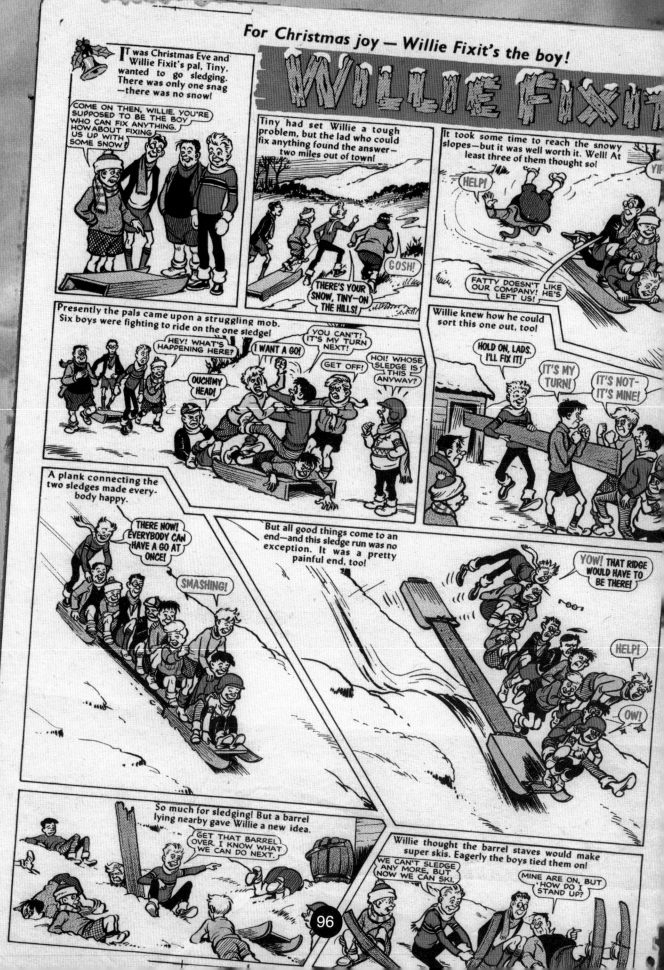

Ha-ha-ha! Ho-ho-ho! — Willie's Christmas present is SNOW!

The skis were a big success—but once again Fatty came a cropper.

GET A MOVE ON, YOU NIT. OH!

HELP!

GROOGH!

Still, everyone had a lot of fun, right up to the time when they had to go home. On their way, the four pals passed the orphanage.

LUCKY LOT! THEY'VE BEEN PLAYING IN THE SNOW!

DID YOU HEAR THAT?

Willie was sorry for the orphanage children. They were all too young to trudge a couple of miles to the hills and back again.

LOOK! IT'S CHRISTMAS DAY TOMORROW. HOW ABOUT GETTING A PRESENT FOR THE ORPHANS? I KNOW WHAT THEY'D LIKE!

When they'd heard Willie's idea, the boys split up and went to collect more help.

MEET OUTSIDE THE STATION AT HALF PAST SIX!

RIGHT, WILLIE.

That evening, nearly all the boys in the street headed out into the hills, and they all had barrows and carties.

KEEP GOING, BOYS. IT'S NOT FAR NOW.

An hour later they were on their way back—with loads of snow!

TAKE IT RIGHT TO THE ORPHANAGE, LADS!

GOOD KING WENCESLAS LOOKED OUT

And on Christmas morning the orphans got the surprise of their lives. Their yard was full of snow!

GOODNESS! HOW DID THAT GET HERE?

YIPPEE!

It was the best present the orphans could have had. And when Willie and his pals came along and joined them in a snow fight, it was the merriest Christmas they had ever had.

HOT MINCE PIES!

OH, BOY! GRUB! YOWF!

TAKE THAT, GREEDY.

OUCH!

WE'VE MADE A SMASHING SLIDE!

FUNNY! THERE'S NO SNOW IN MY GARDEN!

MERRY CHRISTMAS EVERYBODY!

Next week — Fatty is heading for biffs and a bang — When he tries to desert from Willie's gang!

THE Dandy

EVERY TUESDAY

5p

No. 1891
February 18th,
1978.

Building snowcastles, what a great idea by the Dandy scriptwriter.
I'm going to try this next time it snows.

PS – It didn't keep the kids out of trouble. Some of the snowballs missed the snowdan and hit the Mayor.

Spend a **LAUGH-HOUR** with the *BEANO* "funsters"

THE BEANO

2^D

No. 814. Feb. 22nd. 1958.

EVERY THURSDAY

YOU MIGHT AS WELL GIVE UP NOW, BIFFO!

YOU HAVEN'T A HOPE IN THAT THING!

HO-HO! WHAT ARE THE SKIS FOR, BIFFO?

THE WEATHER FORECAST'S NOT GOOD!

MOTORISTS SHOULD BE PREPARED FOR SNOW AND ICE IN MANY PLACES....

CAR RADIO

BIFFO the Bear

YOU'LL NEVER MAKE IT IN THAT MIDGET, BIFFO!

CAR RALLY TODAY. 50-MILE DRIVE

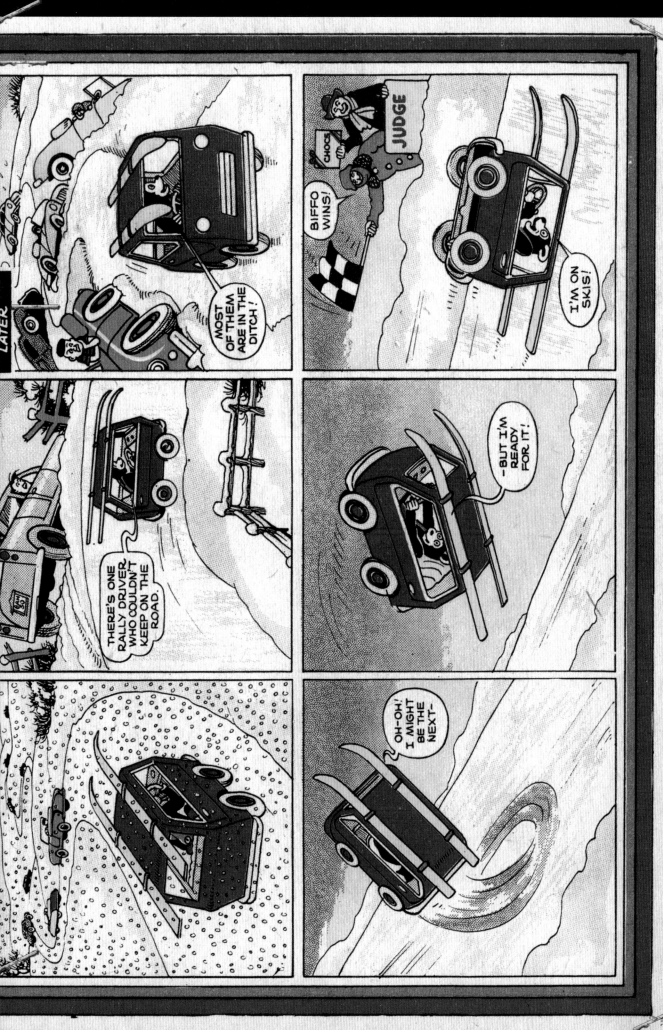

Homemade sledges whizzing down a snow covered city street, not something you would see nowadays. Check out the brave boys in the background – they are wearing shorts!!

THE BEANO

2ᴰ

EVERY THURSDAY   No. 497. JAN. 26th, 1952.

Biffo the BEAR

Aww, Biffo's cousin Bertie is ever so cute. Why didn't we see more of him?

TIN LIZZIE

PROFESSOR PUFFIN has two mechanical servants – Tin Lizzie, the maid, and Brassribs, the butler. They are usually at loggerheads – but not this morning; this was Christmas morning.

TO BERTIE HAPPY XMAS

TO LIZZIE HAPPY XMAS

Tin Lizzie and Brassribs joined Bertie Puffin, the Prof's nephew, to open their Christmas parcels. "Skates!" shrilled Lizzie happily. "Skis!" boomed Brassribs excitedly. "A sledge!" whooped Bertie.

They all went to the park to try out their presents. Brassribs was soon in trouble. He couldn't control his skis. "Help!" he shrieked as he hurtled down the hill.

Arms flailing, Brassribs did a break-neck nose-dive. CRASH! "Ho-ho!" chuckled Lizzie. "Go on! Do it again!"

A beautifully drawn winter story from the Dandy Book 1960. The artist was Jack Prout, more famous for his Black Bob series.

Brassribs took a dislike to skis after that. He reckoned he would get on much better on skates – and he knew where to get a pair.

As Lizzie approached, Brassribs released the branch he had bent back. SWISH! It hit Lizzie amidships, sending her flying backwards ...

... into a tree where she was entangled. Chortling at his success, Brassribs removed the dazed Lizzie's skates.

Then, as cool as you like, he put them on and skated off in great style. Tin Lizzie fumed as she clambered down from the tree.

She would have her revenge! Grimly she tied a rubbery tube from an old cycle wheel between two posts.

Tin Lizzie now had a giant catapult — and the weapon she chose to fire was one of the skis thrown away by Brassribs.

The hurtling ski hit Brassribs such a wallop that the skating butler was rocketed into the air.

Cart wheeling over and over, Brassribs plummet down CRUNCH! Clean through the ice.

Brassribs felt far from cool as he pulled himself out of the freezing water. "Lizzie!" he snarled, his eyes agleam with vengeance.

Picking up the ski that had done the damage, Brassribs charged with it at Lizzie. Lizzie picked up the other ski and charged at Brassribs. Holding the skis like lances, the two pounded towards each other.

"Take that, you brass-neck ruffian!" roared the maid.
"Down with you, you rusty old dish-washer!" rasped Brassribs, breaking his ski against Lizzie's head. Soon both skis were smashed.

Still the battle raged on. Tooth and nail they fought – and they did fearful damage to each other.

Five minutes later it was all over. The battlers had battered each other to pieces. Young Bertie came along. "Gosh!" he gasped. "They look as if they'd been run over by a train!"

Bertie picked up the bits and piled them on his sledge. It would be some job repairing this lot.

Professor Puffin set to work at once. He had done this many times before.

Then he gave them a good, old-fashioned telling off. "Now give Lizzie back her skates, Brassribs!" he finished off. Reluctantly the butler did as he was told.

Poor Brassribs, his Christmas gift was smashed beyond repair. Bertie didn't like to see him left out of the fun, so he borrowed Lizzie's skates and used them, along with the broken skis, to extend his sledge.

Now the sledge was big enough for Tin Lizzie, Brassribs and Bertie. Whooping, they whizzed down the hill. This was great sport, and they were all pals together – for now!

DENNIS the MENACE

Dennis the Menace's first Christmas time in The Beano. The inventive snowballing of the top hats signalled that we had a world class mayhem maker on our hands. This was 1951 and the artist was Davy Law who would be working from the DC Thomson art studio.

The Dandy's own menace, Smasher. This early series of what would become a long running strip was coloured distinctively in blue and yellow. Drawn by Hugh Morren.

THE SMASHER

OH, NO YOU DON'T! YOU'RE NOT GOING OUT—WE'VE HAD TOO MANY COMPLAINTS ABOUT YOU.

AW, DAD!

I'M FED UP—EVERYONE'S HAVING FUN OUTSIDE EXCEPT ME!

WELL, IF THEY WON'T LET ME SLIDE OUTSIDE, I'LL SLIDE INSIDE!

WHEEEE!

GOSH! MUM'S SLIPPED ON MY SLIDE! I'D BETTER SLIDE OFF!

CRASH

SLIP

LATER

THERE'S NO SNOW IN THE HOUSE. I'LL MAKE MY OWN KIND OUT OF FLOUR AND WATER.

FLOUR

HERE WE ARE, LADS! TAKE THAT!

SMASHIN' FUN!

STOP! STOP! YOU'LL HAVE EVERY WINDOW IN THE HOUSE BROKEN!

IT'S NOT ME—IT'S THEM!

DAD LET ME OUT—HE THINKS I'LL DO LESS DAMAGE OUTSIDE THAN INSIDE!

AH! THERE YOU ARE, SMASHER! NOW WE'LL GET YOU!

OOER!

HAVE AT HIM!

LET ME IN! LET ME IN!

THUMP THUMP

YOU WANTED OUT—YOU'LL STAY OUT!

THE OLD LAD WAS IN A TEMPER QUITE
WHEN KORKY TOOK HIS PALING,
BUT NOW THE OLD LAD'S FEELING BRIGHT,
FOR DOWN THE HILL HE'S SAILING.

KORKY THE CAT

Original art boards of Korky the Cat. Colour was applied by brush to the black and white drawings by colourists at the DC Thomson art studio.
The second strip remained in black and white as it was never used. This is the first time it has been seen.
Both drawings by James Crighton who started Korky off in 1937.

Two more original art boards from the sixties. Both have survived fairly intact. The Dennis scene with the snowman army is an all time favourite. The Desperate Dan is a bizarre tale with many twists and turns.

DESPERATE DAN

THERE'S NOTHING LIKE A FIVE MILE STROLL BEFORE BEDTIME IN THE COLD WIND!

THIS WIND IS ICY. LET'S GET HOME QUICK!

OH, BUT IT'S TOO COLD!

HOME AT LAST

WE'LL GET OUR OWN BACK ON THAT BIG BULLY. COME ON UP TO HIS BEDROOM!

YES! WELL LET HIM HAVE PLENTY OF COLD WIND.

I'VE UNSCREWED HIS WINDOW FRAME. NOW WE'LL HIDE IT.

TIME TO GET TO BED! HULLO! SOMEONE'S PINCHED OUR WINDOW FRAME. I'LL BET IT WAS DANNY AND KATEY!

ICY BLAST

YOU'LL BE RIGHT, DAN. I HEARD A SCREWDRIVER TURNING WHEN I CAME IN THE GATE AN HOUR AGO.

IN THE KIDS' BEDROOM

OH WELL, WE'LL TEACH THEM A LESSON. WE'LL PINCH THEIR WINDOW FRAME!

NICE LITTLE DANNY AND KATEY!

HUH!

I'LL FIX IT UP IN OUR BEDROOM, DOG-EARS, THOUGH IT DOESN'T FIT VERY WELL.

FAST ASLEEP

BUT A BLIZZARD SPRINGS UP

MORNING

SWINGING IN THE WIND

SOMETHING KEEPS SCRATCHING MY NOSE. IT'S GOING TO MAKE ME SNEEZE IN A MINUTE!

A-A-TISHOO!

GRR! I KNEW IT!

SNOW BURIED IN IT AND DOG-EARS ISN'T

NO SIGN OF HIM! I'D BETTER BLOW SOME OF THE SNOW AWAY TO SEE IF HE'S UNDERNEATH!

BLOW!

BLAST!

NO! HE'S NOT IN HERE AT ALL!

IN THE KIDS' BEDROOM

NO SIGN OF MY CLOTHES NOW EITHER! IT'S ALL THE FAULT OF DANNY AND KATEY! HI, YOU TWO! OPEN YOUR DOOR!

GROOCH GLUC

NO REPLY! PERHAPS THEY'RE BURIED IN THE SNOW, TOO. I'LL BLOW IT AWAY THROUGH THE KEYHOLE! HERE GOES—

WE'VE BEEN SLEEPING UNDER SNOW ALL NIGHT! BECAUSE SOMEONE HAS PINCHED OUR FRAME! WE'RE BEING BLOWN OUT OF BED.

FOAM

BLOW!

LOOK! WE'VE LANDED ON A HEAP OF SNOW, AND UNCLE DAN'S PAL, DOG-EARS, IS HERE!

WHY, DANNY AND KATEY AREN'T HERE!

Z-Z-Z

AND HERE'S UNCLE DAN'S TROUSERS WITH HIS WALLET IN THE POCKET!

LATER

LOOK AT THAT FUNNY OLD WOMAN AND DOG-EARS MONTANA DRESSED UP IN A HAMMOCK!

OH, THAT'S DESPERATE DAN. HE'S LOST HIS CLOTHES SO HE'S BORROWED HIS GRANNY'S!

DOG-EARS! WE'VE GOT TO FIND THEM KIDS!

DOG-EARS! CAN YOU HEAR THEM KIDS ANYWHERE?

I CAN, DAN! THEY'RE MUNCHING AND LAUGHING, AND KATEY JUST SAID 'WHAT LOVELY BACON AN' EGGS!'

HERE'S WHY—

GOOD JOB UNCLE DAN AIN'T IN HIS H/S OR WE WOULDN'T BE HAVING BREAKFAST IN BED IN THE BEST HOTEL IN TOWN!

-house!

3.2.62

Winker WATSON

SPLOSH!

EE-UGH!

SNOW had fallen at Greytowers School And Winker Watson, the school's wiliest wangler, was making snowballs. Winker decided to let Mr Creep, his Housemaster, have the first sample.

HEY, CREEPY SAW YOU, WINKER — HE'S COMING WITH HIS CANE!

Winker was asking for trouble. But he seemed to expect it!

THANKS, TITCH, I'LL BE READY FOR HIM!

STAY WHERE YOU ARE, WATSON — I'LL DEAL WITH YOU HERE AND NOW!

WHO, ME, MR. CREEP, SIR?

Winker hadn't made a run for it. Why?

Because it would have spoilt the wangle he had prepared for Creepy!

HEE-HEE! YOU OUGHT TO LOOK WHERE YOU'RE GOING, MR. CREEP, SIR!

Winker had laid snow-covered paper on top of the open coal-hole. So instead of enjoying himself caning Winker, Creepy got a big drop!

Now it was the Head's turn for a free sample.

SPLOSH!

UGH! WHO THREW THAT?

WATSON!

Winker had never once been caned. But it seemed certain that his record was about to be broken.

YOU'RE FOR IT, MY LAD!

However, Winker waited hopefully beside the disguised coal-hole. Would that wangle work twice?

EEEK! HELP!

HEE-HEE! MOVE OVER, CREEPY — YOU'VE GOT COMPANY!

The Head plummeted from snowy whiteness into inky blackness!

COME ON, CHAPS, THAT'S GOT RID OF CREEPY AND THE HEAD! LET'S GO OUT AND HAVE SOME FUN!

GOOD OLD WINKER!

WOW! IT'S MILLIGAN'S MOB, WINKER!

QUICK, OVER HERE, BOYS — THERE'S A PILE OF READY MADE SNOWBALLS!

Winker's gate-trick was a smasher — But it failed to stop a high-speed gate-crasher!

THIS IS A BIT OF LUCK, WINKER — I WONDER WHO LEFT THEM HERE?

WE DID! IT WAS A TRAP TO CATCH YOU GREYTOWERS ROTTERS! HEE-HEE-HEE!

Gosh! Winker and his pals had been caught by an outsize wangle!

PLOP!

OW! THEY GOT US, WINKER!

LATER...

LOOK, THERE'S MILLIGAN'S MOB — LET'S PULL A FAST ONE ON THEM!

Winker shouted a challenge to Mick Milligan. The wily wangler wanted revenge.

YAH! MILLIGAN MICROBES! — COME ON, I DARE YOU!

Mounted on their sledges, the toughs came tearing down towards Winker.

HERE THEY COME! HEE-HEE!

At the last minute the wangler shut the gate and made it a dead-end for Milligan's Mob.

THERE! THAT'LL STOP 'EM....

SLAM!

However, the toughs didn't come to the sudden end Winker expected. Mick Milligan's big feet bulldozed the ricketty gate off its hinges!

CRASH!

And they went sledging on, leaving Winker under the wreckage.

...WINKER!

HA-HA-HA!

OOF!

Poor Winker was carried back to school in a groggy state.

HERE'S WATSON! I'LL CANE HIM FIRST...

NO, CREEP, I'M THE HEAD — IT'S MY PRIVILEGE!

Who would get first whack?

NO ONE IS TO CANE THE POOR BOY — HE'S HAD ENOUGH PUNISHMENT FOR ONE DAY!

JUST AS YOU SAY, MATRON — BUT I'LL GET HIM ONE DAY!

GRR!

HEE! HEE!

But no one caned him! Matron stepped in and whipped Winker away. Ha-ha! Good for Winker! He had wangled out of a caning without lifting a finger!

Next week — See how Winker, the wily foxer — Becomes the Greytowers champion boxer.

The adventures of Curly Perkins who spends winter on Marsuvia with his alien pal Jack Silver.
This colour strip was the centre spread of The Dandy in the late seventies. Drawn by Bill Holroyd.

The Zorg troop-carrier roared over a rise, and there, only yards ahead, were Jack and Curly. But the chase wasn't over yet.

KEEP GOING, CURLY!

ALL RIGHT, JACK!

Jack swung his Ski-hound round behind a high rock.

I'VE GOT A JOB FOR YOU, DOGGIE!

A sharp tug on the Ski-hound's reins and the animal did Jack's bidding.

THAT'S RIGHT! BRING DOWN THAT BIG ICICLE!

with his icicle lance, Jack rode the attack like a knight of old.

THIS IS FOR YOU, CAPTAIN ZAPP!

ZOW! HE'S ATTACKING US!

The troop-carrier swerved to dodge Jack's lance, but in doing so, the Zorgs swung under an overhanging rock.

ZEEAGH!

ZAH! THERE GOES OUR JET MOTOR!

ut an engine, the troop-carrier off downhill like a giant sledge.

AIEE! RE GOING ER THAT CLIFF!

ZEEYAH!

ZOWEE!

Over it went! The terrified villains and their troop-carrier hurtled through the icy air.

WHUMF! For the second time that day, the deep snow saved the Zorgs' bacon.

and Curly flew overhead.

ZEH-HEH! I DON'T THINK CAPTAIN ZAPP WILL BE CAUSING ANY MORE TROUBLE, CURLY!

THIS IS ONE CHRISTMAS I WON'T FORGET IN A HURRY, JACK!

The police soon arrived on the scene, but by then Captain Zapp and his henchmen were out of sight, cowering among the snowy rocks to avoid capture.

ZAH! THOSE BRATS HAVE MADE A FOOL OF ME AGAIN! BUT I'LL GET EVEN WITH THEM ONE DAY!

DAN 29.12.79

NEXT WEEK—The funniest fishing trip you've ever seen—The boat that's used is a submarine!

11

This strip from The Topper comic was the opposite from Jack Silver. This time the small spacemen were spending winter on Earth with their friend Jimmy Jones. Drawn by Paddy Brennan.

Fun and surprises with Jimmy Jones and his amazing chums from Space!

1 —In the little fishing-village of Mayport, snow lay thickly on the ground. It was a perfect day for sledging, and that was exactly what Jimmy Jones was about to do. Towing his sledge, and accompied by his three Midget chums from Space, Tik, Tok, and Jok, young Jimmy was making way across the show-covered garden of his house when Pa Jones upset the arrangements. "Not so fast, my lad." he shouted from the doorway.

2—Jimmy's face fell when he saw the big spade in his Dad's hand. " Your mother's got washing to hang out," said Mr Jones cheerfully. " So I want you to clear away all the snow from the garden path and the drying-green before you go off to enjoy yourself." Jimmy gave a big sigh and set to work shovelling snow. He was so glum that he didn't even notice his Midget chums doing some mysterious work behind his back.

3—The Midgets, who had flown in a spaceship from a distant planet to spend a holiday with Jimmy, were planning to help their chum with his labours. They were amazingly clever at inventing queer electrical gadgets, and what they were producing now was a super snow-melting machine. It consisted of an old lamp reflector fitted with a special bulb. Powered by electricity from the Midgets' bodies, it could melt snow like the summer sun.

4—It was the hissing sound coming from the rapidly-melting snow which attracted Jimmy's attention ; the snow was turning into drifting clouds of steam as the scorching ray from the reflector shone on it ! In a few minutes there wasn't a particle of snow left anywhere in Jimmy's garden. But there was still plenty next door, where two children had built a snowman. It was at that moment that a bully came along to spoil the children's fun.

The Midgets know a thing or two—and here's the sort of thing they do!

5—Ben Baker was the bully's name, and he was armed with a mallet, with which he battered the big snow figure to pieces as he leaned over the fence from the street. He thought this was a great joke, and strolled off sniggering while the little boy and girl who had built the snowman sobbed bitterly. The Midgets, meanwhile, were red with rage and hurried to Jimmy's garden shed. They had a plan to teach the rotter a lesson.

6—Jimmy watched in growing amazement as his chums set to work, fixing together pieces from an old bike, parts of a rusty water-tank, and various cogs, wheels and nuts. It seemed impossible, but very soon, the Midgets assembled a metal "man." What was even more amazing, the dummy could actually walk! Jok had made a special control-box, and when he twiddled the knobs on it, the robot strode out of the garden shed.

7—Young Jimmy danced with delight to see the metal man marching smartly across the garden. It didn't take long to discuss with the Midgets the best way of using the robot to tame the bully with the mallet. Jimmy helped to guide the metal figure up on his sledge, then he took over the control-box while the Midgets packed a thick covering of snow over the robot. Now the metal man looked just like an ordinary snowman!

8—"All set?" chuckled Jimmy. "Pile aboard the sledge. I think we'll find that rotter at The Meadows." The youngster towed the sledge for a short distance, then took a seat as they turned on to a piece of waste ground which sloped down to a snow-covered meadow. This was a favourite place for children building snowmen, and sure enough, as the big laden sledge whizzed down the hill, Jimmy spotted Bully Baker up to his dirty tricks.

Bully Baker's smashing plan—doesn't work on the iron man!

9—On the way to the bottom of the slope, Jimmy and the Midgets passed one little girl in tears. Her snowman had already been smashed up by the bully, and he was striding around, swinging his mallet and giving the same treatment to the remaining snowmen in the meadow. Jimmy's sledge slithered to a halt close to a large tree, and the youngster whispered to the Midgets—"Right—we'll leave it here, and hide behind the tree-trunk."

10—Before Bully Baker could spot them, the four chums scurried behind the tree. Seconds later, the bully with the mallet came marching over to deal with the extra-big snowman on the sledge. Jimmy stood ready, having been given final instructions from Jok on how to operate the control-box which guided the movements of the robot's metal arms and legs. And just as Baker raised his mallet, Jimmy pressed the starting button.

11—The bully's mouth fell open and his eyes bulged unbelievingly when the " snowman" suddenly sprang to life. Out jerked a long metal arm to snatch away the mallet from his grasp, and the movement caused most of the snow to fall off the robot's metal body. Bully Baker stood in dismayed horror, unable for a moment to move a muscle. But he found the use of his legs when Jimmy made the robot go lumbering forward!

12—The bully's shrieks of fright echoed round the meadow as he ran for his life with the robot pacing threateningly behind. Everyone laughed to see Bully Baker on the run—and the rotter didn't stop running, even when Jimmy halted the robot. Later on, Jimmy made the metal man assist in rebuilding the shattered snowmen. No wonder the children gave three cheers for Jimmy and the clever Midgets from Space—Tik, Tok and Jok.

A classic to end this collection with. The devilish looking teacher in frame three would have caused laughter in the Beano office as the staff all knew teacher was modelled on Editor George Moonie.

THE BASH STREET KIDS

ON THE WAY TO SCHOOL.

YOWL!

'SCUSE US, TEACHER!

IN THE PLAYGROUND

GRR! STOP THIS NONSENSE, AND CLEAR THE SNOW FROM THE PLAYGROUND INSTANTLY! —IF NOT SOONER!

SPLOSH!

PONK!

PONK!

GLUG!

CRUMP!

SNOW-PLOUGH

BUT CRAFTY TEACHER HAS A PLAN.

BOILER ROOM

QUICK, JANITOR! STOKE UP THAT FIRE! I WANT THE RADIATORS TO BE AS HOT AS POSSIBLE!

YES, BUT LOOK WHERE THEY DUMPED THE SNOW.

JUS' CALL ME SHERPA DANNY!

AVALANCHE

PLODGE!

EEK! IT'S ABOMINABLE!

GRR!

LATER, IN THE STAFF ROOM.

IT PAYS TO BE FIRM WITH THAT MOB, SEE. THEY'VE CLEARED THE SNOW ALREADY!